PROMOTING MENTAL MATHEMATICS

The need to promote mental mathematics has received a lot of curriculum attention in recent years, particularly in terms of providing children with opportunities to discuss the methods that they use. Research* shows that allowing children to explain their mental processes verbally can have a positive effect on their achievements: factual and conceptual knowledge is increased and there is often a marked improvement in pupil confidence. Many teachers now build in time for class or group discussion of mental strategies.

There remains a need, however, for individual consolidation of these strategies. With a whole class to manage, it can be difficult to ensure that each child has an opportunity to explain his or her ideas. Traditionally, many commercial maths schemes present number activities in such a way that the practice of a taught written algorithm is implicit; they do not build on the *mental strategies* that the teacher has been promoting.

CHILDREN TALKING AND WRITING ABOUT THEIR MATHS

Children need to acquire a mathematical vocabulary if they are to become effective mathematicians and have access to the maths problems they encounter in school and outside. This language must be developed systematically. A photocopiable list of some of the mathematical vocabulary that this age group should be using when reflecting on the activities in this book is given on page 6. This list may be particularly valuable for children whose first language is not English. You may also like to refer to the National Numeracy Project booklet *Mathematical Vocabulary* (BEAM).

While children need written maths practice, they also need opportunities to rehearse their developing mental strategies individually. Hence you will find a strong emphasis in these activity sheets on children writing, or talking to each other, about *how* they have done particular calculations or *why* they have reached certain conclusions. This reflection will consolidate the learning, so it is important to value these sections of the sheets. The children's own shorthand terms and phrases are acceptable in this context.

Various classroom strategies could be used to encourage the children to reflect on their maths. These might include: maths-talk partners – with whom to share ideas and answers; adult support – using classroom assistants, or encouraging parents, to talk to the children about their maths work;

maths diaries – for the children to record mathematical activities and to evaluate their own work; follow-up plenaries – in groups, or as a whole class at carpet time, where children can read from their notes and discuss their mental maths strategies.

KNOWING KEY FACTS

Nothing slows down children's development in mental strategies as severely as not having adequate quick recall of the necessary number facts. The activities in this book encourage children to use and apply the facts they already know and to build upon them. For example, a Year 6/Primary 7 child should see that because 7×5 is 35, 7×0.5 is 3.5 and 0.7×0.5 is 0.35 (see page 16). It is essential to check first that children undertaking these activities have a secure store of relevant facts or quick ways of figuring them out; an appropriate test is given on photocopiable page 7 (answers on page 2). A child who completes this test confidently should be ready to tackle the activities in this book.

HOW TO USE THE ACTIVITY SHEETS

These activities are based on recent research* into commonly used mental strategies, and have been designed to be flexible in use. Links are made on each page to activities in the companion teachers' book, *Developing Mental Maths with 9–11 year olds*, from which these photocopiable activities follow. However, these activities will also stand alone; the teachers' notes for each indicate the key mental strategies that are being developed and that should have been introduced beforehand. The activities can be used independently for group work during a class numeracy hour; this will allow the teacher to give more support to another group. The activities provide sound practice in number skills, and could thus be used to enrich a schools maths scheme or as selected homework activities. The teachers' notes indicate ways in which the activity sheets can be modified to provide differentiation and further work; this may involve changing the numbers involved or changing the focus of the questions asked. You can also use the activity sheets provided as models for your own. These activities can be used in any order. A record sheet is given on page 32 to help with planning. It can be photocopied at A3 size for ease of use.

* *The Teaching and Assessment of Number at Key Stages 1–3*, Discussion Paper 10, March 1997, SCAA (Ma/97/762)

KEY FACTS REVIEW, PAGE 2

This test can be used at the start of Year 6 to determine the children's 'readiness' for the activities in this book, which build on the number knowledge and calculation strategies tested here.The page can be photocopied, or the test can be administered to groups orally. In either case, children should be given sufficient time to answer, since this is not intended as a test of speed.

ANSWERS: 1. 156, 200, 219, 1100 **2.** 51, 91, 103, 951 **3.** 17.06, 17.6, 17.61, 17.66

4. Various (accept fractions or decimals) **5.** Various negative numbers **6.** 0.45 **7** 4.8m **8.** Various **9.** Various **10.** 0.5 or ½, 36 **11.** 221 **12.** 188 **13.** 2.3 **14.** 3 **15.** 17, 4½, 13½, 37 **16.** 3 **17.** 0.32 **18.** 1400

COUNTING & ORDERING

BOTH SIDES NOW, PAGE 8

It would be useful preparation to practise counting around the class, in different increments and from different starting points.

KEY STRATEGY: the child needs to recognise and count in regular increments, using whole numbers, decimals and fractions.

MODIFY THE SHEET BY: allowing less confident children to work on one type of example at a time – you could create separate worksheets based on either sets **A** and **B** (whole numbers), sets **C** and **D** (decimals) or sets **E** and **F** (fractions). Include examples of negative numbers on each sheet, so that the children can see that negative numbers can occur with each type of number. More confident children could continue with the count in either direction on a blank sheet of paper, or make up similar sequences for their friends to complete.

ANSWERS: A. 307, 417... 857, 967, 1077 **B.** – 9, – 4, 1... 21, 26 **C.** 4.67, 4.70... 4.82, 4.85, 4.88 **D.** – 5.0, – 4.5, –4.0 ... – 2.0, –1.5 **E.** $2^3/_5$, 3 ... $4^3/_5$, 5, $5^2/_5$ **F.** $-3^3/_4$, –3, $-2^1/_4$... $^3/_4$, $1^1/_2$

OUT OF ORDER, PAGE 9

Some children might find it useful to write the numbers on separate pieces of paper or card, which can then be moved around until the order is correct.

KEY STRATEGY: the child needs to use place value in ordering the numbers.

MODIFY THE SHEET BY: allowing less confident children to work on one type of example at a time. As an extension, ask more confident children to find numbers that fit in between the numbers in each sequence. The 'Extension' ideas for 'Fraction lines' and 'Decimal ladders' in *Developing Mental Mathematics with 9–11 year olds* (p.17) would also be useful extensions to this activity.

ANSWERS: A. 40.44, 44.04, 404.4, 444.4, 4040, 4404, 4440 **B.** 0.006, 0.06, 0.506, 0.56, 0.6, 0.605, 0.65 **C.** – 170, – 71, – 7, 7, 107, 170, 711 **D.** 0.25, 3/4, 4/5, 9/10, 1 1/3, 1.5, 1 3/5.

ACROSS THE LAND, PAGE 10

In order to place this activity in context, the children should use an atlas to locate the countries. When reading large numbers, they should read them as proper numbers – for example, as 'seven million, six hundred and eighty-two thousand, three hundred' rather than as '7-6-8-2-3-0-0'.

KEY STRATEGY: the child should round numbers by focusing on what is significant (for example, rounding to the nearest 1000 by looking at the hundreds number).

MODIFY THE SHEET BY: looking at the 'nearest 1000' for all the numbers first, before going on to look at the 'nearest 100 000'. The activity could be extended by using information books or CD-ROMs to find out the land areas or population figures of other countries. More confident children could also answer or make up questions such as: *Roughly how many times bigger is Australia than Cyprus? How many times bigger is China than New Zealand?*

ANSWERS: Australia 7 682 000, 7 700 000 **Brazil** 8 512 000, 8 500 000 **China** 9 597 000, 9 600 000, **Cuba** 111 000, 100 000 **Cyprus** 9 000, 0 **Ethiopia** 1 097 000, 1 100 000 **Iceland** 103 000, 100 000 **Jamaica** 11 000, 0 **Japan** 378 000, 400 000 **Madagascar** 587 000, 600 000 **New Zealand** 269 000, 300 000 **Pakistan,** 796 000, 800 000 **Sri Lanka** 66 000, 100 000 **United Kingdom** 244 000, 200 000 **Venezuela** 912 000, 1 000 000. In order of land area: China, Brazil, Australia, Ethiopia, Venezuela, Pakistan, Madagascar, Japan, New Zealand, United Kingdom, Cuba, Iceland, Sri Lanka, Jamaica, Cyprus.

WORKING WITH INDICES, PAGE 11

The idea of using index notation (also called standard form) should have been discussed and explored before the children attempt this activity.

KEY STRATEGY: the child needs to understand and apply the logic of 'standard form'.

MODIFY THE SHEET BY: giving all the numbers in standard form to begin with and asking the children to expand them. For extension work, use the land area figures provided on page 10), asking children to write each number in standard form.

ANSWERS: 32 810; thirty-two thousand, eight hundred and ten; 7 990 000; seven million, nine hundred and ninety thousand; 12 070 000; twelve million and seventy thousand; 6.39×10^5; six hundred and thirty-nine thousand; 9.23×10^4; 92 300; 4.89×10^6; four million, eight hundred and ninety thousand; 3.1×10^7; 31 000 000; 2.7865×10^4; twenty-seven thousand, eight hundred and sixty-five; 2.027×10^6; 2 027 000. The completed multiplication grid is shown in Figure 1.

	10 (10^1)	100 (10^2)	1000 (10^3)	10000 (10^4)
10 (10^1)	100 (10^2)	1000 (10^3)	10000 (10^4)	100000 (10^5)
100 (10^2)	1000 (10^3)	10000 (10^4)	100000 (10^5)	1000000 (10^6)
1000 (10^3)	10000 (10^4)	100000 (10^5)	1000000 (10^6)	10000000 (10^7)
10000 (10^4)	100000 (10^5)	1000000 (10^6)	10000000 (10^7)	100000000 (10^8)

Figure 1

ADDITION & SUBTRACTION

HOOPLA SCORES, PAGE 12
Practise adding decimals and fractions verbally with the children before they attempt the sheet.
KEY STRATEGY: the child should use complements of a whole when adding fractions and decimals.
MODIFY THE SHEET BY: having separate sheets for work with fractions and with decimals. Other possible variations include throwing only two rings (simpler), allowing two rings to land on the same number (more complex) and allowing four rings (more complex).
ANSWERS: Toby 26.5, Asma 16.75, Sophie 13½.

FILL THE CORNERS, PAGE 13
Work through some similar examples beforehand.
KEY STRATEGY: the child needs to be able to recompose numbers confidently.
MODIFY THE SHEET BY: providing larger whole numbers as totals, but insisting that the children use at least some decimals or fractions in their answers. Alternatively, fill in one of the corners and ask the children to find numbers for the other three.

TALL STORIES, PAGE 14
This activity gives children the opportunity to contextualise number bonds involving decimals. It also revises various metric units.
KEY STRATEGY: the child needs to use a range of addition and subtraction vocabulary (see page 6).
MODIFY THE SHEET BY: asking less confident children to read out and discuss the stories (or others like them) first, establishing the distinction between addition and subtraction situations. More confident children could try writing their own decimal number stories from scratch.
ANSWERS: 1. 32.3km – 15.8km = 16.5km. **2.** 6.463kg + 5.700kg = 12.163kg. **3.** £9.26 + 1080p = £20.06 (or 2006p). **4.** 5.12m – 386cm = 1.26m (or 126cm).

UPS AND DOWNS, PAGE 15
Provide graph paper for this activity. A –10 to +10 number line would be a useful visual aid.
KEY STRATEGY: the child needs to be able to add and subtract with negative numbers, crossing the 0 where necessary.
MODIFY THE SHEET BY: using only whole-pound values (easier), or using more examples that mix pounds and pence (more difficult). You could introduce the phrase 'in the red' (which originates from the time when bank clerks used red ink for overdrawn accounts); the children could use red pen to mark days when the balance is negative.
ANSWERS: Fiona's balance +£5.00, +£1.00, –£1.00, +£2.00, –£0.50, +£3.00, +£0.25. **Femi's balance** +£5.00, +£1.50, –£1.25, +£1.25, –£1.75, –£3.25, +£6.75.

MULTIPLICATION & DIVISION

DECIMAL WORKOUT, PAGE 16
When they are working on the multiplication grids, encourage the children to explain to you how they are using place value knowledge – for example, '7 × 5 is 35, so 0.7 × 5 is 3.5 because 0.7 is ten times smaller than 7'. It would be useful to prepare the children for the last part of the activity by revising metric measures.
KEY STRATEGY: the child needs to use knowledge of place value to extrapolate from known number facts, and to understand the importance of place value in metric units.
MODIFY THE SHEET BY: using the two parts separately with less confident children. The first task could be extended by drawing up similar tables which include hundreds and hundredths. More confident children could also create their own decimal multiplication and division word problems for a friend to solve.
ANSWERS: 1. 9.6m **2.** 1.4kg **3.** 2.25 litres **4.** 4.2g **5.** 40ml. For the completed multiplication grids, see Figure 2.

MULTIPLES OF 10, PAGE 17
Practise similar questions orally before working on this activity. The children's rules should be expressed in terms of the digits moving left or right relative to the decimal point (which never moves). The rule that you 'add a zero' when multiplying by ten falls down for decimal numbers, and should be avoided: 3.2 × 100 is not 3.200.
KEY STRATEGY: the child needs to recognise the effect on a number of multiplying or dividing by 10.
MODIFY THE SHEET BY: encouraging less confident children to look at multiplying or dividing by 10s, 100s and 1000s only. More confident children could try multiplying by larger multiples of 10 or 100.
ANSWERS: First part 1. 1060, 6500, 8800 **2.** 6000, 45 000, 90 000 **3.** 42, 6, 100.5 **4.** 2680, 432, 26 520 **5.** 4.517, 0.678, 0.016 **6.** 4.65, 0.0129, 0.167 **7.** 2.5, 0.221, 3.13 **8.** 30, 2.4, 42.3. **Second part 1.** ÷ 20 **2.** × 100 **3.** × 30 **4.** ÷ 200 **5.** ÷ 50 **6.** × 200 **7.** ÷ 2000 **8.** × 400.

MORE OR LESS? PAGE 18
Practise similar questions orally before working on this activity. Where the fraction has a numerator other than 1 (as in ¾), it is usually better to divide first and then multiply; but children could also

×	0.5	5	50
0.7	0.35	3.5	35
7	3.5	35	350
70	35	350	3500

×	0.3	3	30
1.6	0.48	4.8	48
16	4.8	48	480
160	48	480	4800

×	1.2	12	120
0.4	0.48	4.8	48
4	4.8	48	480
40	48	480	4800

Figure 2

investigate the effect of first multiplying and then dividing – the answer should be the same, and this may serve as a useful way of checking.
KEY STRATEGY: the child needs to relate fractional quantities to division and recognise the fractional equivalents of percentages.
MODIFY THE SHEET BY: including only unit fractions to simplify the activity.
ANSWERS: 1. $\frac{1}{8}$ of 200 **2.** $\frac{3}{4}$ of 80 **3.** $\frac{1}{2}$ of 56 **4.** $\frac{1}{6}$ of 330 **5.** 75% of 36 **6.** 25% of 380 **7.** 50% of 98 **8.** They are the same.

LEFTOVERS, PAGE 19
A quick session on verbal recall of times tables would be a useful warm-up for this activity; include division questions, such as 32 ÷ 4 = ? As a follow-up, the children could go on to page 22, or play the game 'Quotient & remainder' from *Developing Mental Mathematics with 9–11 year olds* (p.43).
KEY STRATEGY: the child should use recall of times table facts, and spot patterns in the remainders table.
MODIFY THE SHEET BY: starting with easier divisions (by 2 and by 3). More confident children could be asked to state how they knew which divisions gave particular remainders.
ANSWERS: 14, 20; 26, 32, 38; 62, 68, 74, 80, 92, 98; 11, 18, 25; 32, 39, 46; 32, 46.

LARGE NUMBER NEWS, PAGE 20
A general discussion of the differences between tabloid and broadsheet newspapers would be useful to contextualise this activity. The children will need to be told the height of the classroom.
KEY STRATEGY: the child should use the estimates to check that her/his answers are sensible.
MODIFY THE SHEET BY: reading out and discussing the problems with less confident children. Different pairs of children could also be given different questions to investigate.

MULTIPLE CROSSING-OUT, PAGE 21
This activity is a useful way to revise several aspects of number including multiples, factors and tests of divisibility.
KEY STRATEGY: the child should look for patterns of multiples.

MODIFY THE SHEET BY: extending the grid to 200 and asking children to cross out multiples of 11, 13, 17 and 19.
ANSWERS: The numbers remaining are 1, 2, 3, 5, 7, 11, 13, 17, 19, 23, 29, 31, 37, 43, 47, 53, 59, 61, 67, 71, 73, 79, 83, 89, and 97.

MORE LEFTOVERS, PAGE 22
The activity 'Leftovers' (p.19) should be completed prior to this activity.
KEY STRATEGY: the child needs to see the connections between remainders, fractions and decimals in solving division problems.
MODIFY THE SHEET BY: focusing initially on two of the ways to write remainders, rather than all three (however, all three need to be considered before going on to the word problems).
ANSWERS: 1. 50 r 1, 50.5, 50½ **2.** 13 r 1, 13.33, 13 1/3 **3.** 24 r 1, 24.25, 24¼ **4.** 16 r 7, 16.7, 16 7/10 **5.** 43 r 3, 43.6, 43 3/5 **6.** 12 r 3, 12.375, 12 3/8 **7.** 28 r 3, 28.75, 28¾ **8.** 17 r 3, 17.5, 17½ **9.** 13 r 1 **10.** £3.25 **11.** 1½ **12.** 10 **13.** 34.8kg **14.** 15 r 2

MULTISTEP & MIXED OPERATIONS

THE MISSING SIGNS, PAGE 23
Go through some similar examples orally as preparation. If children get stuck, encourage them to experiment: the answers can be found by trial and improvement.
KEY STRATEGY: the child needs to predict the effects of different operations.
MODIFY THE SHEET BY: putting in one of the missing signs (to simplify the task).
ANSWERS: 1. × and + **2.** ÷ and – **3.** – and ÷ **4.** – and + **5.** × and ÷ **6.** × and ÷ **7.** × and – **8.** + and ÷ **9.** × and ÷ **10.** + and –

NUMBER SORT, PAGE 24
Review the difference between a factor and a multiple before the children attempt this activity.
KEY STRATEGY: the child should use knowledge of multiplication patterns.
MODIFY THE SHEET BY: using only the two-circle Venn diagram with less confident children.
ANSWERS: see Figure 3.

FUNCTION CIRCUITS, PAGE 25
Introduce this activity by drawing a large blank 'circuit' on the board and discussing an example. Point out that the circuit can be completed from any starting point.

KEY STRATEGY: the child should predict the effects of different operations, and use inverse operations to check her/his answers.

MODIFY THE SHEET BY: filling in some of the missing numbers or operations (to simplify the task). More confident children could be asked to create larger circuits incorporating six or more stages.

ANSWERS: (from top left, clockwise) **1.** 9, 36, 18, ÷ 3 **2.** 350, ÷ 5, 35, × 10 **3.** – 20, + 100, × 4, – 310 (**or** ÷ 32) **4.** × 4, + 39 (**or** × 2.5), 0.65, × 10.

NEW YEAR SALE, PAGE 26

A general discussion about shop sales will help to set the context. Follow up this activity with the game 'Shop 'til you drop' from *Developing Mental Mathematics with 9–11 year olds* (p.56).

KEY STRATEGY: the child should use fractional equivalents (1/4 and 1/5) to calculate percentage decreases.

MODIFY THE SHEET BY: asking less confident children to calculate the effect of a 50% discount.

ANSWERS: 1. £12.00 **2.** £4.50 **3.** £9.75 **4.** £6.75 **5.** £14.40 **6.** £20.00 **7.** £5.60 **8.** £4.40

FOOTWEAR FUN, PAGE 27

The children need to have some experience of drawing and interpreting pie charts before attempting this activity.

Provide angle measurers and graph paper. The activities 'Theatre attendance' and 'Forestation' in *Developing Mental Mathematics with 9–11 year olds* (p.50 and p.52) would be useful for follow-up work on the interpretation of data.

KEY STRATEGY: the child should realise that there is a connection between the 'piece' size (or sector) on the pie chart and the number of children in that category.

MODIFY THE SHEET BY: enlarging the pie charts, to help children measure the angles more accurately. More confident children could carry out a survey into their classmates' footwear, perhaps using a data handling program to generate pie charts.

ANSWERS: 1. Boots: 10, Sandals: 1, Shoes: 4, Trainers: 3. **2.** Black: 6, Blue: 3, Brown: 4, Yellow: 5.

BUS ROUTES, PAGE 28

Revise the 24-hour clock with the children before they attempt this activity.

KEY STRATEGY: the child needs to work systematically in order to avoid confusing units of distance, time and money.

MODIFY THE SHEET BY: altering the timetable to include only multiples of 5 (minutes) as time intervals. More confident children could use local timetable and fare information to set and answer questions.

ANSWERS: Route 1. 09:30, 09:50, 10:05, 10:23, 10:47, 11:02, 11:20, 11:35, 11:59, 12:17, 12:32, 12:52 **Route 2** 14:30, 14:50, 15:05, 15:23, 15:47, 16:02, 16:20, 16:35, 16:59, 17:17, 17:32, 17:52 **Route 3** 19:20, 19:40, 19:55, 20:13, 20:37, 20:52, 21:10, 21:25, 21:49, 22:07, 22:22, 22:42 **Bus fares: 1.** £2.40 **2.** £2.00 **3.** £2.10 **4.** £2.10 **5.** £3.60

STRICTLY AVERAGE, PAGE 29

Discuss the difference between the three types of average (mean, median and mode) beforehand.

KEY STRATEGY: the child needs to check (by estimation) that her/his answers are sensible.

MODIFY THE SHEET BY: presenting the two parts on separate sheets. The table could be simplified by including only multiples of 10 in the scores.

ANSWERS: Original scores mean = 2, mode = 2, median = 2. **Modified scores** mean = 3, mode = 2, median = 2. The most likely mean number of goals per game at the end of the season is about 2 (the score of 10 being a 'freak' result). **Weekly mean scores: 1.** 38.75 **2.** 52.5 **3.** 55 **4.** 52.5 **5.** 45 **6.** 45 **7.** 62.5 **8.** 48.75 **9.** 56.25 **10.** 36.25. **Team mean scores: Blues** 51.5 **Reds** 49 **Greens** 46 **Yellows** 50.5. The overall mean is 49.25.

BRING ON THE BRACKETS, PAGE 30

Discuss the convention of BODMAS (Brackets Over Division, Multiplication, Addition and Subtraction) as a class beforehand.

KEY STRATEGY: the child's mental calculation needs to follow the order determined by the brackets.

MODIFY THE SHEET BY: including only strings of three numbers (easier) or including examples with five or more single-digit numbers (more difficult).

ANSWERS: 1. 3 × (4 + 6); 48 ÷ (6 – 2) **2.** 2 × (3 + 6) × 2

LONELY MATHS, PAGE 31

The cards can be cut out and used for a matching game.

KEY STRATEGY: the child needs to use mental strategies in all four operations with confidence.

MODIFY THE SHEET BY: focusing on only two of the operations, or leaving out the decimal examples. More confident children could make up a similar game using fractions or decimals throughout.

ANSWERS: 500 – 220 and 5 × 7 × 8 = 280; 55 × 8 and 1000 – 560 = 440; 75 × 4 and 3000 ÷ 10 = 300; 11 – 1.01 and 999 ÷ 100 = 9.99; 76 ÷ 100 and 1 – 0.24 = 0.76; 990 + 99 and 2000 – 911 = 1089; 98 + 666 and 1100 – 336 = 764; 97 + 205 and 3.02 × 100 = 302; 99 × 9 and 1010 – 119 = 891; 1009 – 670 and 678 ÷ 2 = 339. The 'odd ones out' are 34 × 6 (204), 1010 ÷ 10 (101), 777 + 707 (1484) and 1000 – 125 (875).

Figure 3

MATHS WORD LIST

approximately	hundred thousands	product
average	hundredths	quotient
brackets	in between	remainder
complement	index/indices	sign
cubes/cubic	inverse	sixths
numbers	kilogram	square numbers
decimal point	litre	ten thousands
denominator	mean	tenths
digit	median	thirds
discount	metre	thousands
eighth	mode	thousandths
equivalent	million	times
estimate	multiple	timetable
factor	negative number	total
fifths	numerator	treble
fraction	operation	twice
greater than	order	units
graphs	pattern	value
horizontal	percentage	Venn diagram
how much longer	pie chart	vertical
how much heavier	prime numbers	zero

NAME _____   DATE _____

KEY FACTS REVIEW

1. What is 120 more than:

36? _____   80? _____

99? _____   980? _____

2. What is 49 fewer than:

100? _____   140? _____

152? _____   1000? _____

3. Put these numbers in increasing order of size:

17.6   17.06   17.66   17.61

_____ _____ _____ _____

4. Write down any two numbers between 13 and 14:

_____ _____

5. Write down any two numbers less than zero:

_____ _____

6. Which is bigger, $\frac{2}{5}$ or 0.45? _____

7. Which is longer, 4.8m or 408cm?

_____

8. Find two different ways to make 113 using addition:

☐ + ☐ + ☐ + ☐ = 113

☐ + ☐ + ☐ + ☐ = 113

9. Find two different ways to make 112 using subtraction:

☐ – ☐ = 112

☐ – ☐ = 112

10. Find the missing numbers:

$160 \div 10 =$ ☐ $\times 32$

$110 -$ ☐ $= 0.74 \times 100$

11. $174 + 47 =$ ☐

12. $212 - 24 =$ ☐

13. $0.5 + 0.6 + 0.9 + 0.3 =$ ☐

14. $10 - 2.5 - 3 - 1.5 =$ ☐

15. What is:

double 8.5? _____

treble $1\frac{1}{2}$? _____

half of 27? _____

a quarter of 148? _____

16. $100 \times 0.03 =$ ☐

17. $3.2 \div 10 =$ ☐

18. $70 \times 20 =$ ☐

BOTH SIDES NOW

■ For each sequence, write in the missing numbers before and after the three numbers given.

A

| _____ | _____ | 527 | 637 | 747 | _____ | _____ | _____ |

B

| _____ | _____ | _____ | 6 | 11 | 16 | _____ | _____ |

C

| _____ | _____ | _____ | 4.73 | 4.76 | 4.79 | _____ | _____ |

D

| _____ | _____ | _____ | −3.5 | −3.0 | −2.5 | _____ | _____ |

E

| _____ | _____ | $3\frac{2}{5}$ | $3\frac{4}{5}$ | $4\frac{1}{5}$ | _____ | _____ | _____ |

F

| _____ | _____ | _____ | $-1\frac{1}{2}$ | $-\frac{3}{4}$ | 0 | _____ | _____ |

✏ On the back of the sheet, explain how you decided which numbers were missing in each sequence.

☺ Which sequence did you find easiest to complete? Which was the most difficult one? Tell a friend.

SEE DEVELOPING MENTAL MATHS WITH 9–11 YEAR OLDS 'CARRY ON COUNTING' P.12

Counting and ordering

NAME _____   DATE _____

OUT OF ORDER

■ The numbers in each set have got mixed up. Can you write them in order, from the smallest to the largest?

A

4040	444.4	4404	4440	44.04	404.4	40.44

____ ____ ____ ____ ____ ____ ____

B

0.506	0.56	0.605	0.006	0.06	0.65	0.6

____ ____ ____ ____ ____ ____ ____

C

107	–7	–170	7	170	–71	711

____ ____ ____ ____ ____ ____ ____

D

$\frac{3}{4}$	1.5	0.25	$\frac{4}{5}$	$1\frac{1}{3}$	$\frac{9}{10}$	$1\frac{3}{5}$

____ ____ ____ ____ ____ ____ ____

✏ On the back of the sheet, write some instructions showing how to work out the order for each set of numbers.

SEE DEVELOPING MENTAL MATHS WITH 9–11 YEAR OLDS 'ORDER, ORDER!' P.13

PRACTISING MENTAL MATHS

ACROSS THE LAND

■ This table shows the land area (in square kilometres) of fifteen countries. Fill in the third and fourth columns of the table by writing the land areas to the nearest 1000 and the nearest 100 000 sq.km.

Country	Land area (sq.km)	Nearest 1000	Nearest 100 000
Australia	7 682 300		
Brazil	8 511 965		
China	9 596 960		
Cuba	110 860		
Cyprus	9 251		
Ethiopia	1 096 900		
Iceland	103 030		
Jamaica	10 957		
Japan	377 535		
Madagascar	587 041		
New Zealand	268 680		
Pakistan	796 100		
Sri Lanka	65 600		
United Kingdom	244 100		
Venezuela	912 100		

■ List the fifteen countries in order of size:
1. China   2. _____

_____

_____

Discuss these questions with your partner:
• What is important when you are approximating numbers to the nearest 1000 or the nearest 100 000?
• Why might the information in the table be approximate anyway?
• Why is there a problem with resolving the two smallest countries to the nearest 100 000?

SEE DEVELOPING MENTAL MATHS WITH 9–11 YEAR OLDS 'LIBRARIES' P.15

WORKING WITH INDICES

■ Complete this table showing numbers in three forms: using index notation, as full numbers and in words.

Index notation	Full number	In words
4.67×10^5	467 000	Four hundred and sixty-seven thousand
3.281×10^4		
7.99×10^6		
1.207×10^7		
	639 000	
		Ninety-two thousand three hundred
	4 890 000	
		Thirty-one million
	27 865	
		Two million twenty-seven thousand

■ Now complete this multiplication grid, writing each number both as a full number and using index notation.

	10 (10^1)	100 (10^2)	1000 (10^3)	10 000 (10^4)
10 (10^1)	100 (10^2)			
100 (10^2)		10 000 (10^4)		
1000 (10^3)				
10 000 (10^4)				

 Why is index notation useful for writing large numbers?

 Can you see a rule for multiplying indices? Do you think there might be a similar rule for dividing indices? Discuss with a friend.

SEE DEVELOPING MENTAL MATHS WITH 9–11 YEAR OLDS 'INDEX NOTATION' P.16 AND 'READ A BIG ONE' P.12

NAME _____   DATE _____

HOOPLA SCORES

Three friends went to the funfair and had a go at the hoopla stall.
They each had three rings to throw at a hoopla board. Each ring had
to land on a different number.

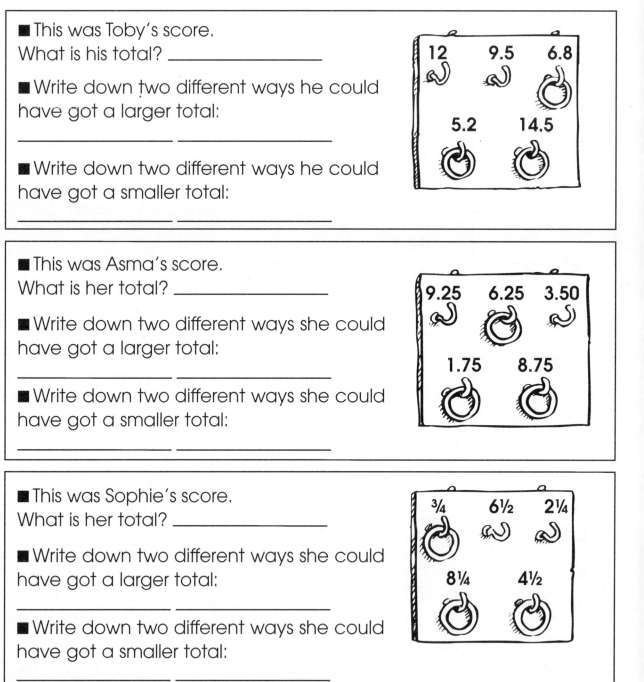

■ This was Toby's score.
What is his total? _____

■ Write down two different ways he could
have got a larger total:

_____ _____

■ Write down two different ways he could
have got a smaller total:

_____ _____

Toby's board: 12   9.5   6.8   5.2   14.5

■ This was Asma's score.
What is her total? _____

■ Write down two different ways she could
have got a larger total:

_____ _____

■ Write down two different ways she could
have got a smaller total:

_____ _____

Asma's board: 9.25   6.25   3.50   1.75   8.75

■ This was Sophie's score.
What is her total? _____

■ Write down two different ways she could
have got a larger total:

_____ _____

■ Write down two different ways she could
have got a smaller total:

_____ _____

Sophie's board: ¾   6½   2¼   8¼   4½

✏ Choose one of the questions and explain how you knew that your
ways of making larger and smaller totals worked. Write on the back
of this sheet.

SEE DEVELOPING MENTAL MATHS WITH 9–11 YEAR OLDS 'FAIRGROUND FUN' P.23 AND 'ADDITION OF FRACTIONS' P.25

FILL THE CORNERS

■ In each of these boxes, write four numbers in the corners to give the total in the centre. You cannot use a 0, but you may use fractions, decimals or negative numbers. Find three different ways to make each total.

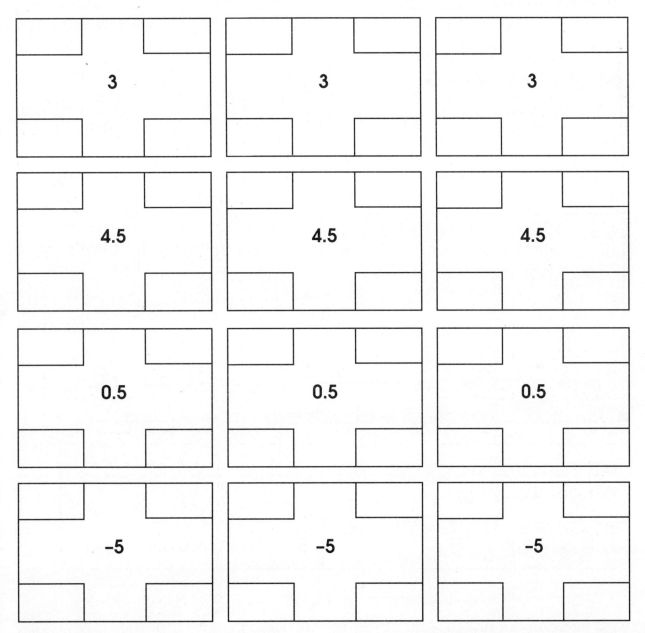

 Swap with a friend and check each other's answers. Look at where you have made a total in different ways, and explain to each other why you chose those ways.

SEE DEVELOPING MENTAL MATHS WITH 9–11 YEAR OLDS 'FENCE IT IN' P.24, 'ADDITION OF FRACTIONS' P.25

ADDITION AND SUBTRACTION

TALL STORIES

■ Write an appropriate number sentence for each of these stories. Include the answers.

1. Pete cycled 15.8km after lunch. If his whole day's journey was 32.3km, how far had he gone before stopping for lunch?	**2.** Tony's bag for the school trip weighed 6.463kg; Ashok's weighed 5.700kg. What was the total weight of their bags?
3. Joy collected £9.26 for the sponsored walk; Becky collected 1080 pence. How much did they collect between them?	**4.** In the triple jump, Ber jumped 5.12m and Carol jumped 386cm. How much longer was Ber's jump?

■ Now make up a story for each of these number sentences. Write on the back of the sheet.

5. 5.65 + 3.92 = 9.57	**6.** 9.2 – 3.6 = 5.6
7. 11.60 – 6.85 = 4.75	**8.** 8.756 + 0.800 = 9.556

Read through your stories carefully. Can you be sure that they really match the number sentences, or could someone else interpret them differently?

When you are sure they are right, swap stories with a friend. Do you agree on what number sentence each story means?

SEE DEVELOPING MENTAL MATHS WITH 9–11 YEAR OLDS 'HOW MUCH MORE?' P.24

ADDITION AND SUBTRACTION

UPS AND DOWNS

Help Fiona and Femi to manage their money for a week by filling in their cash balance at the end of each day.

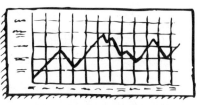

Fiona's week

	Balance
Saturday Receive £5.00 pocket money.	+£5.00
Sunday Spend £4.00 on cinema trip.	+£1.00
Monday Buy new Boyzik single for £2.00.	–£1.00
Tuesday Present of £3 from Aunt Carla.	
Wednesday Spend £2.50 on flowers for Gran.	
Thursday Cut neighbour's lawn for £3.50.	
Friday Buy comic and sweets for £2.75.	

Femi's week

	Balance
Saturday Receive £5.00 pocket money.	+£5.00
Sunday Spend £3.50 on seaside trip.	
Monday Buy new pencil case for £2.75.	
Tuesday Sell unwanted toy for £2.50.	
Wednesday Buy Uncle Sid a book for £3.00.	
Thursday Give £1.50 to charity collection.	
Friday Draw £10 from bank savings.	

 How can you check your answers? Is there more than one way?

Ask your teacher for some graph paper. Draw line graphs to show how Fiona's and Femi's cash balances went up and down.

SEE DEVELOPING MENTAL MATHS WITH 9–11 YEAR OLDS 'MINUS MINUS' P.26

DECIMAL WORKOUT

×	0.5	5	50
0.7			
7			
70			

■ Complete this multiplication grid:

■ What patterns do you notice?

■ Now complete these tables, again looking for patterns:

×	0.3	3	30
1.6			
		48	
160			

×	1.2		
0.4			
4			480
40		480	

Talk to a friend.
Can you explain these patterns?

■ Shade in the right answer for each of these word problems:

1. What is the total length of 8 strips of wood if each is 1.2m long?

96m	9.6m	0.96m

2. What is the total weight of 7 packets of sweets if each weighs 200g?

140g	0.14kg	1.4kg

3. What is the total capacity of 9 cups if each holds 250ml?

2.25 litres	22 500ml	22.5 litres

4. What is the weight of 1 marble if 100 marbles weigh 0.42kg?

42g	4.2g	0.042kg

5. How much lemonade will each child get if 1.7 litres is shared between 5 children?

0.034 litres	34ml	340ml

Check through your answers.
Are you sure they are all sensible?

SEE DEVELOPING MENTAL MATHS WITH 9–11 YEAR OLDS 'MULTIPLY IT OUT' P.32

MULTIPLES OF 10

■ Work out the three multiplications or divisions in each box.

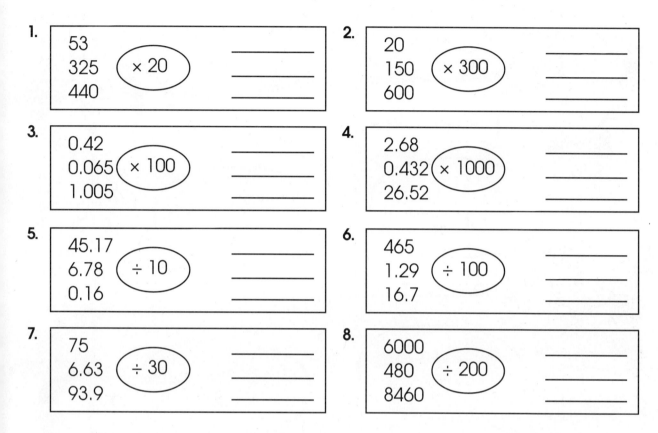

1.
53
325 (× 20) _____
440   _____
                _____

2.
20
150 (× 300) _____
600   _____
                _____

3.
0.42
0.065 (× 100) _____
1.005   _____
                 _____

4.
2.68
0.432 (× 1000) _____
26.52   _____
                  _____

5.
45.17
6.78 (÷ 10) _____
0.16   _____
               _____

6.
465
1.29 (÷ 100) _____
16.7   _____
                 _____

7.
75
6.63 (÷ 30) _____
93.9   _____
               _____

8.
6000
480 (÷ 200) _____
8460   _____
                _____

■ Complete these number sentences by multiplying or dividing by a multiple of 10.

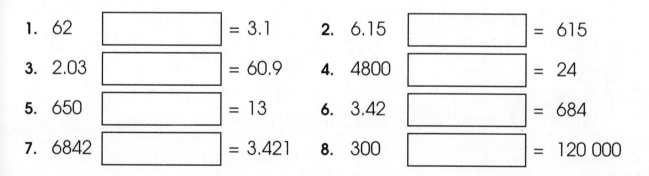

1. 62 [____] = 3.1   2. 6.15 [____] = 615

3. 2.03 [____] = 60.9   4. 4800 [____] = 24

5. 650 [____] = 13   6. 3.42 [____] = 684

7. 6842 [____] = 3.421   8. 300 [____] = 120 000

 What rule can you use to multiply or divide by 10 or 100? How can you use this rule to help you multiply by **a multiple** of 10 or 100? Discuss your rules with your teacher. Do they work for any number?

SEE DEVELOPING MENTAL MATHS WITH 9–11 YEAR OLDS 'MULTIPLYING & DIVIDING BY POWERS OF 10' P. 32, 'FUNCTION MACHINES' P.33

MORE OR LESS?

■ Which is more...

1/7 of 140 or 1/8 of 200?

1. _____

2/3 of 75 or 3/4 of 80?

2. _____

1/3 of 81 or 1/2 of 56?

3. _____

3/5 of 90 or 1/6 of 330?

4. _____

75% of 36 or 10% of 250?

5. _____

50% of 184 or 25% of 380?

6. _____

3/4 of 64 or 50% of 98?

7. _____

20% of 120 or 1/3 of 72?

8. _____

How can you check your answers? Is there more than one way?

On the back of this sheet, make a list of all the equivalent fractions and percentages that you know. Use these to make up some more problems like the ones above. Give them to your friends.

SEE DEVELOPING MENTAL MATHS WITH 9-11 YEAR OLDS 'FRACTIONAL QUANTITIES' P.33, 'CALCULATING PERCENTAGES' P.35

LEFTOVERS

■ Complete this table showing what the remainder will be for each division.

	Divide by 4	Divide by 5	Divide by 6	Divide by 7	Divide by 8	Divide by 9
11	3	1	5			
12	0					
13	1					
14						
15						
16						
17						
18						
19						
20						
21						
22						
23						
24						
25						

 What do you notice about the largest possible remainder in each column?

 Discuss these questions with a friend:

* Which numbers give a remainder of 2 when dividing by 6?
* What will the next three numbers in this sequence be?
* Which of these numbers give a remainder of 2 when dividing by 6?
  62 67 68 71 72 74 80 84 85 92 98

* Which numbers give a remainder of 4 when dividing by 7?
* What will the next three numbers in this sequence be?
* Which of these numbers give a remainder of 4 when dividing by 7?
  32 35 37 40 46 51 56 59 65 72 86

SEE DEVELOPING MENTAL MATHS WITH 9–11 YEAR OLDS 'SEVEN AND A BIT' P.34, 'REMAINDERS' P.40

NAME

DATE

LARGE NUMBER NEWS

Compare two newspapers: one tabloid and one broadsheet.

■ First estimate the answers to the following questions, then find reasonably accurate answers. Use blank paper for working out.

How many words are there on a typical page of each newspaper?

_____ _____

How many words are there in the whole of each newspaper?

_____ _____

How many more words are there in the broadsheet than the tabloid?

_____ _____

How many words does each paper print in one week? In one month? In one year?

_____

_____

How many letters are there on a typical page of each of the newspapers?

_____ _____

How many pages of each newspaper will cover the floor of your classroom?

_____ _____

How many pages of each newspaper will cover the floor of your school hall?

_____ _____

How many copies of each newspaper do you need to make a pile that reaches from the floor to the ceiling?

_____ _____

How did you decide what was a typical page?

How accurate do you think each answer was? On the back of the sheet, make a list of all the approximations you made.

SEE DEVELOPING MENTAL MATHS WITH 9–11 YEAR OLDS 'IN MY LIFE' P.37

MULTIPLICATION AND DIVISION

MULTIPLE CROSSING-OUT

1	2	3	4	5	6	7	8	9	10
11	12	13	14	15	16	17	18	19	20
21	22	23	24	25	26	27	28	29	30
31	32	33	34	35	36	37	38	39	40
41	42	43	44	45	46	47	48	49	50
51	52	53	54	55	56	57	58	59	60
61	62	63	64	65	66	67	68	69	70
71	72	73	74	75	76	77	78	79	80
81	82	83	84	85	86	87	88	89	90
91	92	93	94	95	96	97	98	99	100

■ Go through this grid systematically, crossing out multiples of 2 (but not 2 itself). Use a light-coloured pencil.

■ What do you notice about the multiples of 4? What about the multiples of other even numbers?

_____

■ Now cross out the multiples of 3 (but not 3 itself), using a different-coloured pencil.

■ Look at the multiples of 9. Why are they all already crossed out?

_____

■ Now cross out all the remaining multiples of 5 and 7 (but not 5 and 7 themselves), using another different-coloured pencil.

■ What numbers are left? _____

Why are these numbers left? Explain to a friend.

Draw a 101–200 number square on squared paper. Investigate the pattern of multiples of the same numbers you tried before.

SEE DEVELOPING MENTAL MATHS WITH 9–11 YEAR OLDS 'PRIME SIEVE' P.38

MORE LEFTOVERS

Remember! Remainders can be written in three ways. For example:
$7 \div 2 = 3 \text{ r } 1$ or 3.5 or $3\frac{1}{2}$

■ For each of these division questions, write the answer in three ways.

1. $101 \div 2 =$ _____

2. $40 \div 3 =$ _____

3. $97 \div 4 =$ _____

4. $167 \div 10 =$ _____

5. $218 \div 5 =$ _____

6. $99 \div 8 =$ _____

7. $115 \div 4 =$ _____

8. $105 \div 6 =$ _____

■ Now solve the following problems:

9. Four children share 53 marbles.
How many marbles does each child get?

10. Four children share £13 equally.
How much money does each child get?

11. Four children share 6 small pizzas.
How much pizza does each child get?

12. If children sit three to a seat on a bus trip,
how many seats does a class of 29 children need?

13. If the total mass of five children is 174kg, what is their average mass?

14. A teacher shares 92 coloured pencils between six tables of children. How many pencils does she leave on each table?

In each of these division problems, there is 'a bit left over'. Discuss with a friend whether you used a remainder, a fraction or a decimal in each case, and why that was the best choice.

SEE DEVELOPING MENTAL MATHS WITH 9–11 YEAR OLDS 'DECIMAL REMAINDERS' P.41

NAME

DATE

THE MISSING SIGNS

■ Fill in the missing operation signs in each of these number sentences. In each case, explain how you found the sign.

1. 18 ☐ 4 ☐ 28 = 100 How I did it:	2. 96 ☐ 3 ☐ 13 = 19 How I did it:
3. 303 ☐ 285 ☐ 4 = 4.5 How I did it:	4. 20 ☐ 22 ☐ 5 = 3 How I did it:
5. 3.7 ☐ 5 ☐ 18.5 = 1 How I did it:	6. 720 ☐ 10 ☐ 100 = 72 How I did it:
7. 7 ☐ 7 = 100 ☐ 51 How I did it:	8. 19.5 ☐ 7.5 = 81 ☐ 3 How I did it:
9. 91 ☐ 10 = 9100 ☐ 10 How I did it:	10. −7 ☐ 3 = 81 ☐ 85 How I did it:

 Which problems were easy to work out? Which were more difficult? Does your friend agree?

On the back of the sheet, make up 8 questions like those above for your friend to solve.

SEE DEVELOPING MENTAL MATHS WITH 9–11 YEAR OLDS 'MISSING OPERATION' P. 46

PRACTISING MENTAL MATHS

DATE

NUMBER SORT

■ Complete these Venn diagrams.

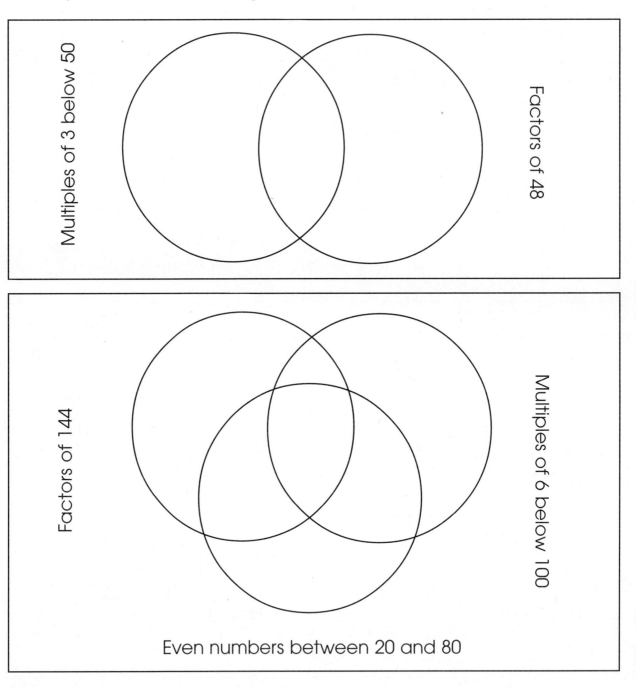

MULTISTEP AND MIXED OPERATIONS

 What can you say about the numbers in the overlapping areas? Discuss with a friend.

On the back of the sheet, create another Venn diagram puzzle using your own criteria. Give it to your friend.

SEE DEVELOPING MENTAL MATHS WITH 9–11 YEAR OLDS 'WHAT'S MY RULE?' P.47

FUNCTION CIRCUITS

In the circuits below, numbers go in circles: ○
and operations go in squares: ▢

■ Go around each circuit in a clockwise direction, putting in the
missing numbers and operations. You must end up back where you
started.

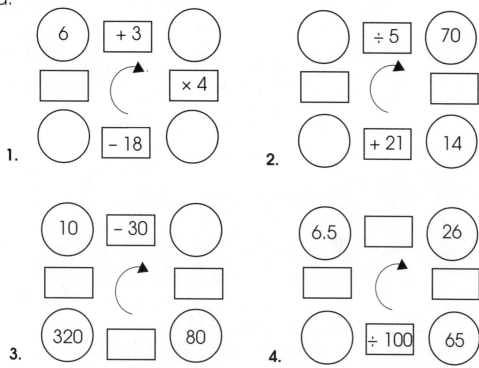

1.

2.

3.

4.

■ Now make up two circuits of your own.

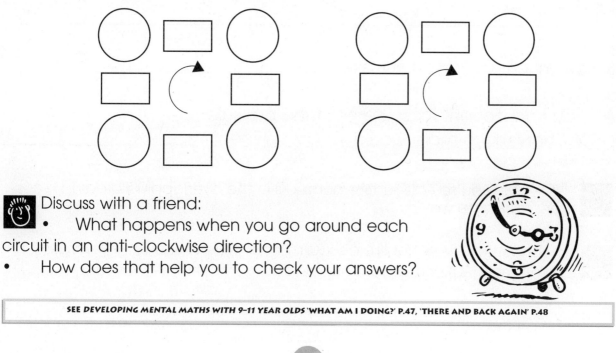

Discuss with a friend:
•   What happens when you go around each
circuit in an anti-clockwise direction?
•   How does that help you to check your answers?

SEE DEVELOPING MENTAL MATHS WITH 9–11 YEAR OLDS 'WHAT AM I DOING?' P.47, 'THERE AND BACK AGAIN' P.48

MULTISTEP AND MIXED OPERATIONS

MULTISTEP AND MIXED OPERATIONS

NEW YEAR SALE

GROUND FLOOR: 25% DISCOUNT

FANPLASTIC NEW YEAR SALE

■ Calculate the sale price of each item:

1. DJ BEETLE Double album CD *My Shell* £16.00 →
2. SUGAR BOYZ Remix CD single *Love So Sweet* £6.00 →
3. THE CALCULATORS Album CD *We Can Work It Out* £13.00 →
4. MC BAD GUY Album cassette *Truly Badly Cheaply* £9.00 →

1ST FLOOR: 20% DISCOUNT

■ Calculate the sale price of each item:

5. Stereo headphones £18.00 →
6. Fanplastic personal stereo £25.00 →
7. Sugar Boyz poster £7.00 →
8. CD rack (holds 20 CDs) £5.50 →

■ You have £40 to spend on up to four items. What would you buy?

_____

■ How much would you have left over? _____

■ If you had bought these items at the pre-sale
prices, how much more would you have spent? _____

 Discuss with a friend how you solved these problems. Did you both do
them the same way?

 How would you work out the discount prices if the amounts were larger
(more than £100) or awkward numbers like £3.99 or £7.49? Tell your teacher.

SEE DEVELOPING MENTAL MATHS WITH 9–11 YEAR OLDS 'PRICE CHANGE' P.49

FOOTWEAR FUN

A survey found out what footwear eighteen children were wearing:

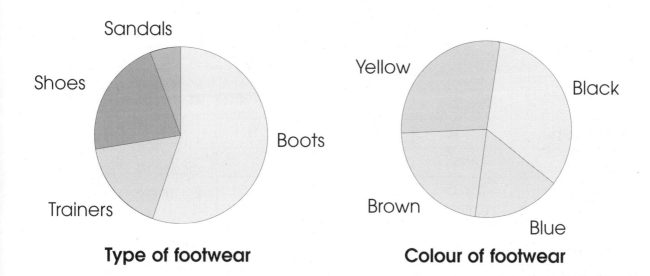

Type of footwear   **Colour of footwear**

■ Use an angle measurer and rough paper to help you work out how many children had footwear in each category:

Type	Boots: ____	Sandals: ____	Shoes: ____	Trainers: ____
Colour	Black: ____	Blue: ____	Brown: ____	Yellow: ____

■ Ask your teacher for some squared paper. Draw up a bar graph for each of these sets of data.

■ Use the data below, from the same survey, to create a bar graph and a pie chart:

Fastening	Buckle: 2	Laces: 7	Slip-ons: 3	Velcro: 5	Zip: 1

Compare your bar graphs to the pie charts. What questions could you use each to answer? Write them on the back of this sheet.

A further child is found to be wearing black trainers with laces. How could you add this information to the bar graphs and pie charts? What is difficult about updating the pie charts? Tell your teacher.

SEE DEVELOPING MENTAL MATHS WITH 9–11 YEAR OLDS 'INTERPRETING PIE CHARTS' P.49

MULTISTEP AND MIXED OPERATIONS

BUS ROUTES

A bus travels from Aville to Freemore and back three times a day.

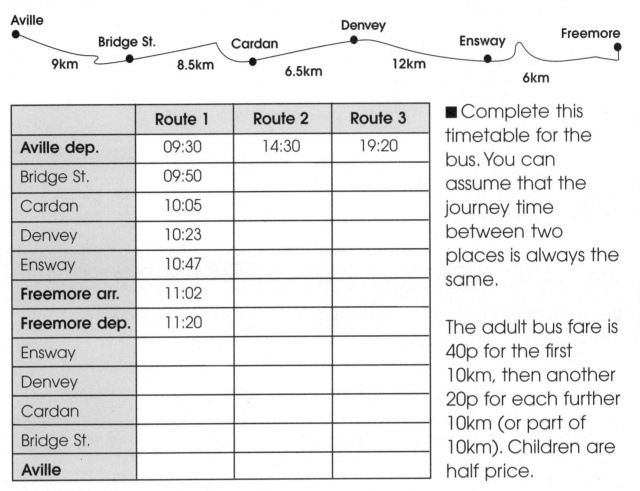

	Route 1	Route 2	Route 3
Aville dep.	09:30	14:30	19:20
Bridge St.	09:50		
Cardan	10:05		
Denvey	10:23		
Ensway	10:47		
Freemore arr.	11:02		
Freemore dep.	11:20		
Ensway			
Denvey			
Cardan			
Bridge St.			
Aville			

■ Complete this timetable for the bus. You can assume that the journey time between two places is always the same.

The adult bus fare is 40p for the first 10km, then another 20p for each further 10km (or part of 10km). Children are half price.

■ Working on the back of the sheet, find the total cost of the following:

1. Three adults travelling from Aville to Denvey.
2. One adult and two children travelling from Bridge Street to Freemore.
3. Two adults and three children travelling from Cardan to Ensway.
4. One adult and five children travelling from Freemore to Denvey.
5. Two adults and two children travelling from Freemore to Aville.

 Check your answers with a friend. Compare your methods for working out the calculations.

Why are the answers to questions **3** and **4** the same?

SEE *DEVELOPING MENTAL MATHS WITH 9–11 YEAR OLDS* 'RAIL TRAVEL' P.50

STRICTLY AVERAGE

■ In their first seven games of the season, a football team scored 2, 3, 2, 2, 1, 0 and 4 goals. Find the mean, median and mode of the scores.

MEAN = _____ MEDIAN = _____ MODE = _____

■ In their eighth game, they scored 10. Find the new averages:

MEAN = _____ MEDIAN = _____ MODE = _____

What has changed? What has stayed the same? Why does that happen? Discuss with a friend.

Can you estimate the likely mean number of goals per game scored by this team at the end of the season?

■ This table shows the house points scored by four school teams during a ten-week period. Find the mean number of points per team in each week, and the mean number of points per week scored by each team. Use rough paper for working out.

	BLUES	REDS	GREENS	YELLOWS	Weekly mean
Week 1	45	50	30	30	38.75
Week 2	60	80	40	30	
Week 3	80	60	50	30	
Week 4	35	25	70	80	
Week 5	60	20	75	25	
Week 6	30	25	35	90	
Week 7	90	55	30	75	
Week 8	50	45	40	60	
Week 9	50	70	80	25	
Week 10	15	60	10	60	
Mean					

Work out the mean of the four teams' average weekly scores (the bottom row), while your friend works out the mean of the weekly mean scores for all the teams (the right-hand column). Are they the same? Why?

SEE DEVELOPING MENTAL MATHS WITH 9-11 YEAR OLDS 'AVERAGE SCORES' P.52

BRING ON THE BRACKETS

Do you remember how the order in which a series of operations is carried out affects the answer?

■ Which of these pairs gives the larger result?

$$3 \times (4 + 6) \quad \text{or} \quad (3 \times 4) + 6$$
$$48 \div (6 - 2) \quad \text{or} \quad (48 \div 6) - 2$$

■ Which of these three sequences gives the largest result?

$$(2 \times 3) + (6 \times 2) \quad \text{or} \quad 2 \times (3 + 6) \times 2 \quad \text{or} \quad 2 \times (3 + (6 \times 2))$$

■ Investigate the effect of putting one or two pairs of brackets in different places in the following expressions. (Each expression is given three times, so you can try different versions.)

$10 \times 3 \div 6 + 9 =$	$10 \times 3 \div 6 + 9 =$	$10 \times 3 \div 6 + 9 =$
$8 + 3 \times 6 + 7 =$	$8 + 3 \times 6 + 7 =$	$8 + 3 \times 6 + 7 =$
$4 \times 7 - 2 \times 5 =$	$4 \times 7 - 2 \times 5 =$	$4 \times 7 - 2 \times 5 =$
$27 \div 3 + 6 \times 2 =$	$27 \div 3 + 6 \times 2 =$	$27 \div 3 + 6 \times 2 =$

■ Now use the number sequences below, with any operations and at least one pair of brackets, to investigate the different effects of using brackets. (Each number sequence is given three times.)

5 10 4 5 =	5 10 4 5 =	5 10 4 5 =
18 6 3 9 =	18 6 3 9 =	18 6 3 9 =
30 5 15 10 =	30 5 15 10 =	30 5 15 10 =

Talk to your teacher about 'BODMAS'. Have all of your number sentences followed this convention?

SEE DEVELOPING MENTAL MATHS WITH 9–11 YEAR OLDS 'I'M THINKING OF A NUMBER' P.46

LONELY MATHS

■ Pair up the number sentences below that give the same answer. You should end up with four unpaired number sentences. Use the empty boxes at the bottom to make up partners for these four 'loners'.

75 × 4	97 + 205	55 × 8	76 ÷ 100
11 – 1.01	34 × 6	1010 ÷ 10	990 + 99
98 + 666	1 – 0.24	1009 – 670	500 – 220
2000 – 911	3000 ÷ 10	1100 – 336	3.02 × 100
99 × 9	777 + 707	678 ÷ 2	999 ÷ 100
1000 – 125	1000 – 560	1010 – 119	5 × 7 × 8

Which number sentences were easy to find the right partners for? Which were more difficult?

Does your friend agree?

SEE *DEVELOPING MENTAL MATHS WITH 9–11 YEAR OLDS* 'NUMBER SENTENCES' P.54

MULTISTEP AND MIXED OPERATIONS

TEACHERS' RECORD SHEET

NAMES	COUNTING & ORDERING				ADDITION & SUBTRACTION				MULTIPLICATION & DIVISION							MULTISTEP & MIXED OPERATIONS								
	BOTH SIDES NOW, P8	OUT OF ORDER, P9	ACROSS THE LAND, P10	WORKING WITH INDICES, P11	HOOPLA SCORES, P12	FILL THE CORNERS, P13	TALL STORIES, P14	UPS AND DOWNS, P15	DECIMAL WORKOUT, P16	MULTIPLES OF 10, P17	MORE OR LESS?, P18	LEFTOVERS, P19	LARGE NUMBER NEWS, P20	MULITPLE CROSSING-OUT, P21	MORE LEFTOVERS, P22	THE MISSING SIGNS, P23	NUMBER SORT, P24	FUNCTION CIRCUITS, P25	NEW YEAR SALE, P26	FOOTWEAR FUN, P27	BUS ROUTES, P28	STRICTLY AVERAGE, P29	BRING ON THE BRACKETS, P30	LONELY MATHS, P31
1																								
2																								
3																								
4																								
5																								
6																								
7																								
8																								
9																								
10																								
11																								
12																								
13																								
14																								
15																								
16																								
17																								
18																								
19																								
20																								
21																								
22																								
23																								
24																								
25																								
26																								
27																								
28																								
29																								
30																								
31																								
32																								
33																								
34																								
35																								